THE COMPLETE ORGAN PLAYER BEATLES

Wise Publications
London/New York/Sydney

Exclusive Distributors:
Music Sales Limited
8/9 Frith Street,
London W1V 5TZ, England.
Music Sales Pty Limited
120 Rothschild Avenue,
Rosebery, NSW 2018,
Australia.

This book © Copyright 1992 by Wise Publications
Order No.NO90454
ISBN 0-7119-2994-7

Cover designed by Pearce Marchbank Studio
Compiled by Peter Evans
Music arranged by Kenneth Baker
Music processed by MSS Studios

Music Sales' complete catalogue lists thousands of
titles and is free from your local music shop, or direct from Music Sales Limited.
Please send a cheque/postal order for £1.50 for postage to:
Music Sales Limited, Newmarket Road, Bury St. Edmunds,
Suffolk IP33 3YB.

Your Guarantee of Quality
As publishers, we strive to produce every book to the highest
commercial standards.
The music has been freshly engraved and the book has been
carefully designed to minimise awkward page turns and to make
playing from it a real pleasure.
Particular care has been given to specifying acid-free, neutral-sized
paper which has not been chlorine bleached but produced with
special regard for the environment. Throughout, the printing and
binding have been planned to ensure a sturdy, attractive
publication which should give years of enjoyment.
If your copy fails to meet our high standards, please inform us and
we will gladly replace it.

Printed in the United Kingdom by
J.B. Offset Printers (Marks Tey) Limited, Marks Tey, Essex.

WHEN I'M SIXTY FOUR
Words & Music by John Lennon & Paul McCartney

Upper: trumpet
Lower: flutes + piano
Pedal: 8′
Drums: swing

YESTERDAY
Words & Music by John Lennon & Paul McCartney

Upper: flute
Lower: flutes
Pedal: bass guitar
Drums: 8 beat

TICKET TO RIDE
Words & Music by John Lennon & Paul McCartney

Upper: guitar
Lower: flutes
Pedal: bass guitar
Drums;8 beat

♩ = 120

IF I FELL
Words & Music by John Lennon & Paul McCartney

Upper: string ensemble
Lower: flutes
Pedal: 8'
Drums: 8 beat

♩ = 90

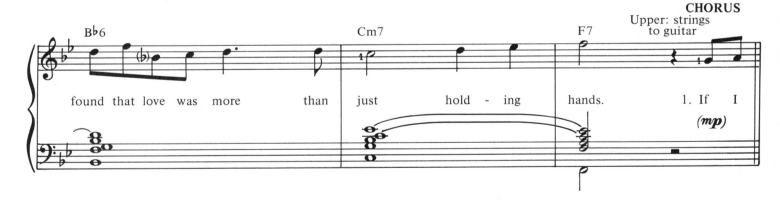

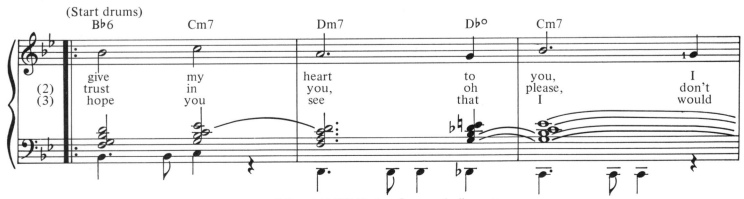

10

stop drums

I WANNA BE YOUR MAN

Words & Music by John Lennon & Paul McCartney

Upper: brass ensemble
Lower: flutes + piano
Pedal: bass guitar
Drums: rock

THIS BOY
Words & Music by John Lennon & Paul McCartney

Upper: flute + piano + sustain
Lower: flutes + piano
Pedal: 8'
Drums: slow rock

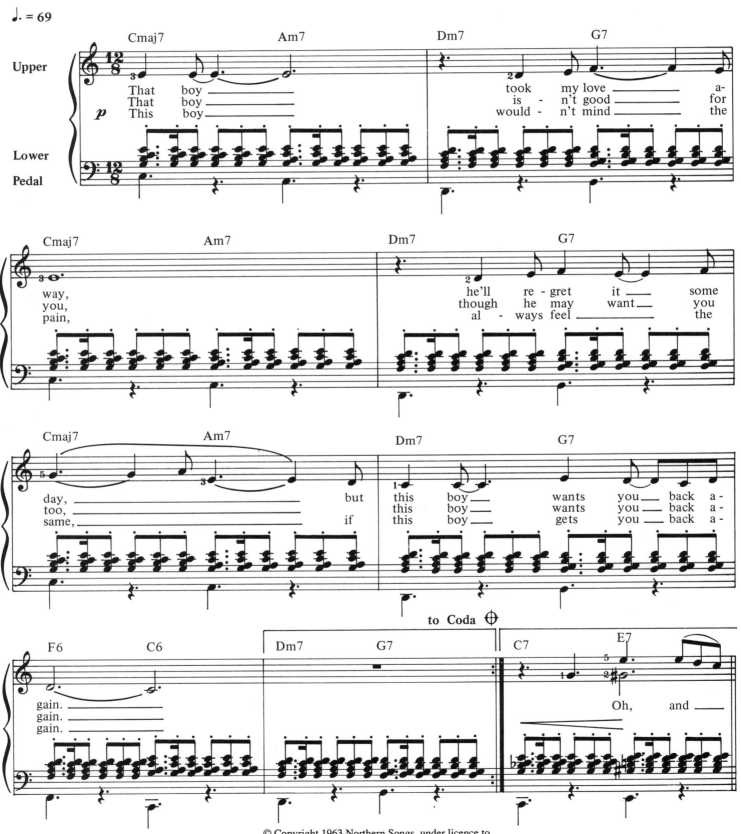

OB-LA-DI, OB-LA-DA
Words & Music by John Lennon & Paul McCartney

Upper: full organ
Lower: flutes + piano
Pedal: 16' + 8'
Drums: 8 beat

to Coda ⊕

la — la how the life goes on.

INTERLUDE
Upper: cut piano

In a cou - ple of years they have built a home, —

— sweet home.

With a cou - ple of

18

kids run - ning in the yard of

Des - mond and Mol - ly Jones.

And if you want some fun,

Take ob - la - di - bla - da.

stop drums

19

THE FOOL ON THE HILL
Words & Music by John Lennon & Paul McCartney

Upper: flute
Lower: flutes
Pedal: bass guitar
Drums: 8 beat

♩ = 72

Day af-ter day, a-lone on a hill, the man with the fool-ish grin is keep-ing
Well on the way, head in a cloud, the man of a thou-sand voi-ces talk-ing

per-fect-ly still. But no-bo-dy wants to know him, they can see that he's just a fool.___ And
per-fect-ly loud. But no-bo-dy ev-er hears him, or the sound he ap-pears to make.___ And

he nev-er gives an an-swer, but the fool___ on the hill sees the sun go-ing down,___ and the
he nev-er seems to no-tice, but the fool___ on the hill sees the sun go-ing down,___ and the

eyes in his head ___ see the world spin-ning round. ___
eyes in his head ___ see the world spin-ning round. ___

HEY JUDE
Words & Music by John Lennon & Paul McCartney

Upper: synth.
Lower: flutes
Pedal: bass guitar
Drums: 8 beat

♩ = 88

DAY TRIPPER
Words & Music by John Lennon & Paul McCartney

Upper: trumpet
Lower: flutes + piano
Pedal: bass guitar
Drums: rock

♩ = 138

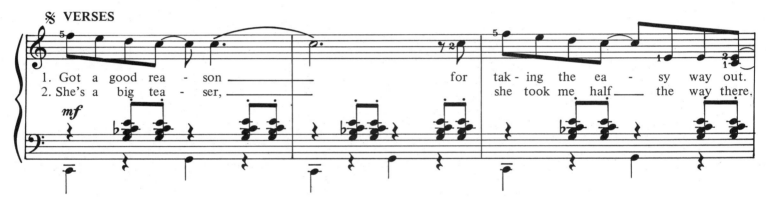

1. Got a good rea - son for tak - ing the ea - sy way out.
2. She's a big tea - ser, she took me half the way there.

Upper: add guitar
CHORUS

tak - ing the ea - sy way out.
she took me half the way there. She was a day

WE CAN WORK IT OUT

Words & Music by John Lennon & Paul McCartney

Upper: piano
Lower: flutes
Pedal: bass guitar
Drums: 8 beat

♩ = 92

GIRL

Words & Music by John Lennon & Paul McCartney

Upper: organ (with chorale)
Lower: flutes + piano
Pedal: bass guitar
Drums: swing

29

A HARD DAY'S NIGHT
Words & Music by John Lennon & Paul McCartney

Upper: saxophone
Lower: flutes + piano
Pedal: bass guitar
Drums: rock

YOU'VE GOT TO HIDE YOUR LOVE AWAY

Words & Music by John Lennon & Paul McCartney

Upper: harpsichord + flute
Lower: flutes
Pedal: bass guitar
Drums: slow rock

and I hear them say.
let me hear you say.

CHORUS

Hey, you've got to hide your love a - way.

Hey, you've got to hide your love a - way.

stop drums

LADY MADONNA
Words & Music by John Lennon & Paul McCartney

Upper: guitar + organ
Lower: flutes + piano
Pedal: bass guitar
Drums: rock

♩ = 108

CAN'T BUY ME LOVE
Words & Music by John Lennon & Paul McCartney

Upper: brass ensemble
Lower: flutes
Pedal: 8'
Drums: swing

♩ = 160

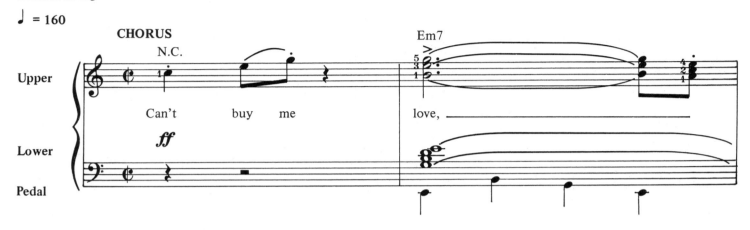

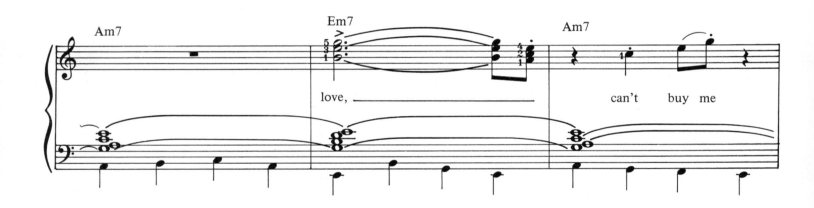

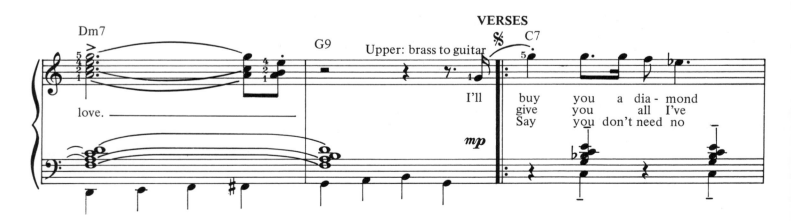

SGT. PEPPER'S LONELY HEARTS CLUB BAND

Words & Music by John Lennon & Paul McCartney

Upper: trumpet
Lower: flutes
Pedal: bass guitar
Drums: rock

♩ = 112

SHE LOVES YOU
Words & Music by John Lennon & Paul McCartney

Upper: brass ensemble
Lower: flutes
Pedal: bass guitar
Drums: rock

♩ = 132

you she's think-ing of, _____ and she told me what to
now she says she knows _____ you're not the hurt-ing
Pride can hurt you too, _____ a- pol - o - gise to

say - yi - yay. She says she
kind. _____ She says she loves you, and you know that can't be
her. _____ Be - cause she

bad, _____ yes, she loves you, and you

cresc.

know you should be glad. _____

f   *mp*

2. She

CHORUS
Upper: guitar to brass

Ooh!   She loves you, yeh,   yeh, yeh! _____ She

43

CHORD CHARTS (For Left Hand)

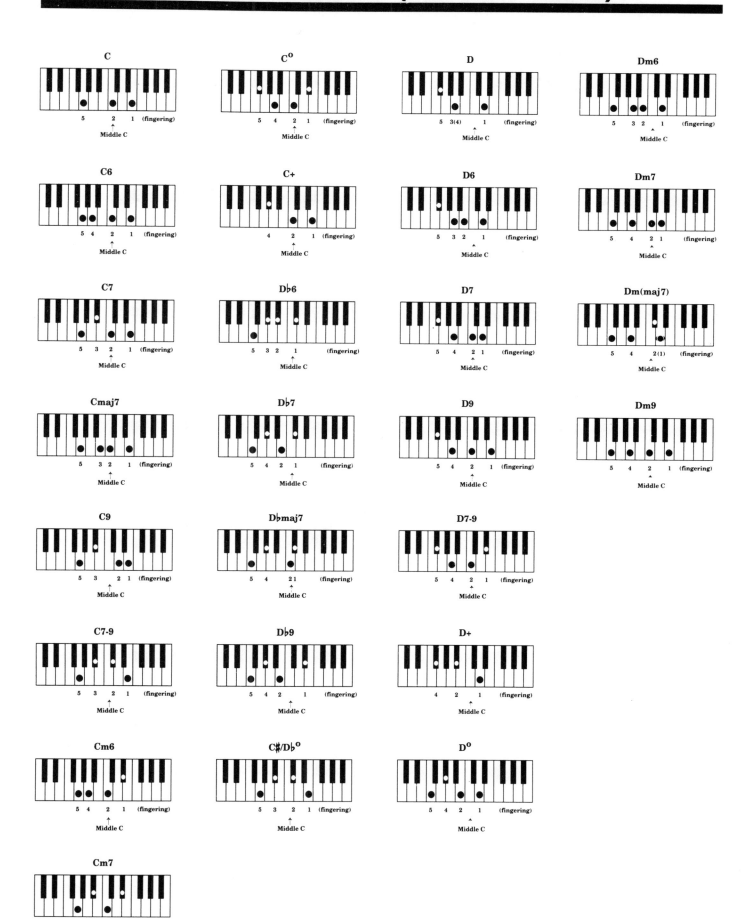

CHORD CHARTS (For Left Hand)

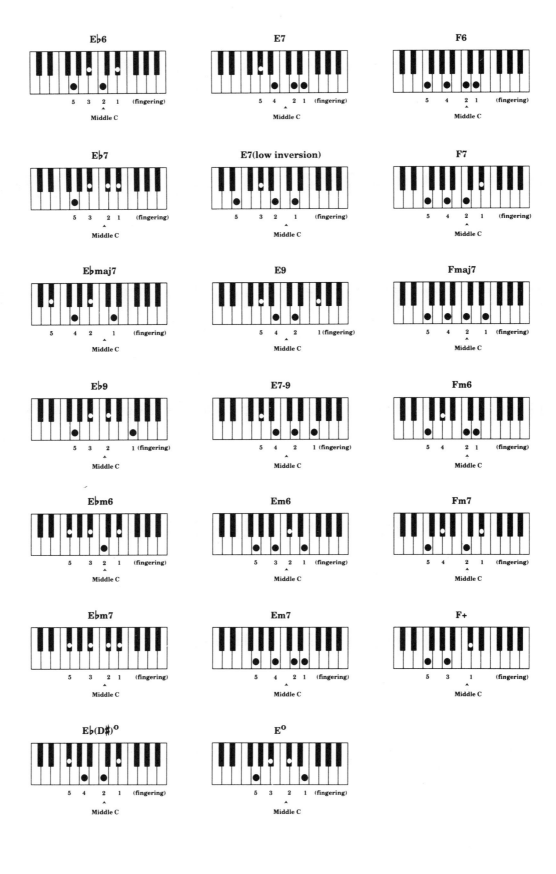

CHORD CHARTS (For Left Hand)

G♭6
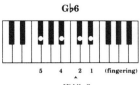
5 4 2 1 (fingering)
▲
Middle C

G
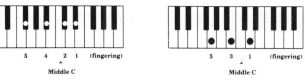
5 3 1 (fingering)
▲
Middle C

Gm
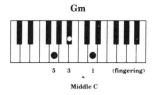
5 3 1 (fingering)
▲
Middle C

A♭
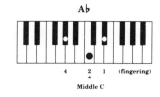
4 2 1 (fingering)
▲
Middle C

F♯(G♭)7
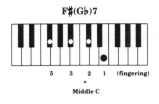
5 3 2 1 (fingering)
▲
Middle C

G6
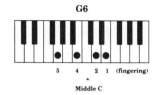
5 4 2 1 (fingering)
▲
Middle C

Gm6
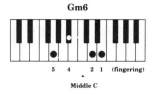
5 4 2 1 (fingering)
▲
Middle C

A♭6
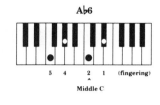
5 4 2 1 (fingering)
▲
Middle C

F♯m7
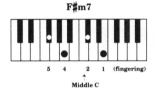
5 4 2 1 (fingering)
▲
Middle C

G7
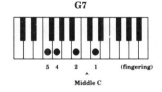
5 4 2 1 (fingering)
▲
Middle C

Gm7
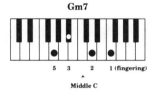
5 3 2 1 (fingering)
▲
Middle C

A♭7
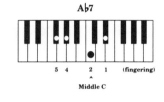
5 4 2 1 (fingering)
▲
Middle C

F♯°
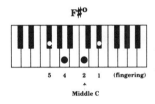
5 4 2 1 (fingering)
▲
Middle C

G7(high inversion)
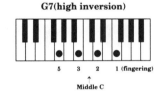
5 3 2 1 (fingering)
▲
Middle C

Gm7(low inversion)
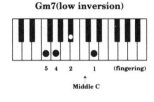
5 4 2 1 (fingering)
▲
Middle C

A♭maj7
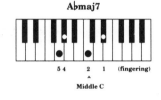
5 4 2 1 (fingering)
▲
Middle C

Gmaj7
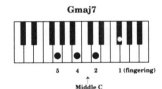
5 4 2 1 (fingering)
▲
Middle C

Gm(maj7)
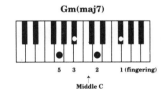
5 3 2 1 (fingering)
▲
Middle C

A♭m7
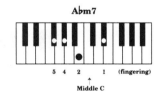
5 4 2 1 (fingering)
▲
Middle C

G9
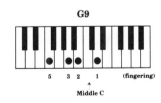
5 3 2 1 (fingering)
▲
Middle C

A♭m6
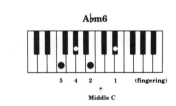
5 4 2 1 (fingering)
▲
Middle C

G7-9
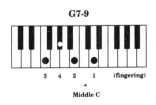
5 4 2 1 (fingering)
▲
Middle C

A♭(G♯)°
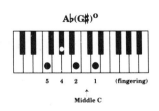
5 4 2 1 (fingering)
▲
Middle C

G+
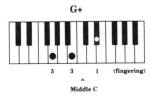
5 3 1 (fingering)
▲
Middle C

CHORD CHARTS (For Left Hand)

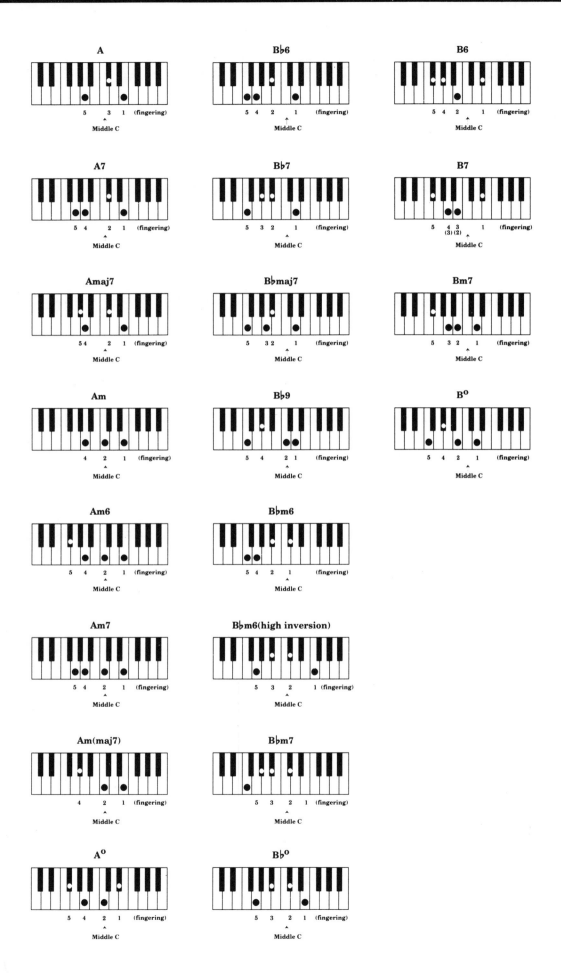